Classic Albums

COLOURING

BOOK

Classic Albums Colouring Book

First published: August 2016

This work © Red Planet Publishing Ltd 2016

Paperback ISBN: 978 1 9059 5993 8

The right of Mark Young to be identified as author of this Work has been asserted by him in accordance with sections 77 and 78 of the Copyright, Designs and Patents Act 1988

Thanks to **www.thisdayinmusic.com** for their assistance with the text of this book

For more information visit: www.redplanetzone.com

Printed and bound by CPI Group (UK) Ltd, Croydon, CR0 4YY

Classic Albums

COLOURING BOOK

Jefferson Airplane

During August and September 1972, Jefferson Airplane recorded their second live album, *Thirty Seconds Over Winterland*, at the Auditorium Theatre in Chicago and the Winterland Ballroom in San Francisco. The psychedelic rock group had achieved massive success with hits such as 'Somebody to Love' and the classic *Alice in Wonderland*-inspired 'White Rabbit', thanks in no small part to the distinctive vocals of singer Grace Slick.

Having played at all the legendary Sixties festivals – Woodstock, Altamont, Monterey and the Isle of Wight – they had become a fantastic live band. The Winterland was given an extra poignancy by the death of the group's old friend, Janis Joplin, from a heroin overdose the previous day. The intensity of their performances belies the fact that band would split up the following year, essentially turning into different groups: Jefferson Starship and Hot Tuna.

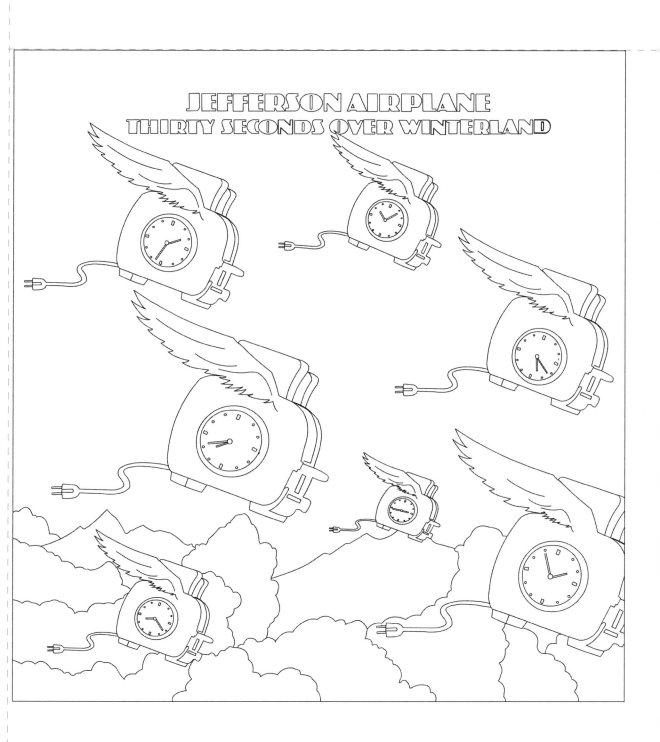

DE LA SOUL

One of the most innovative groups to emerge from the 1980s hip-hop scene, De La Soul took rap in a whole new direction on their debut album, *3 Feet High and Rising*. Their lyrics were cryptic and playful, their rapping was laid-back and conversational. Even when tackling social problems such as drug addiction, they maintained a thoughtful lightness of touch. Helped considerably by their visionary producer, Prince Paul, De La Soul's music sampled Steely Dan, The Turtles and even French-language tuition albums with quirky, but always funky, results.

Although the trio quickly tired of being labelled the 'hippies of hip-hop', the distinctiveness of *3 Feet High and Rising* has made it many people's favourite hip-hop album.

QUICKSILVER MESSENGER SERVICE

Formed in 1965, Quicksilver Messenger Service became lynchpins of the San Francisco psychedelic scene alongside Jefferson Airplane and Moby Grape. *Happy Trails* was their second album, and was recorded mostly live at two performances – one at the Fillmore East, one at the Fillmore West. It featured John Cipollina and Gary Duncan on guitars, David Freiberg on bass and Greg Elmore on drums. All contributed vocals.

The first side of the album consists of the 'Who Do You Love Suite' – extended, blues-rock improvisations on Bo Diddley's R'n'B song 'Who Do You Love'. The album's title track is a cover of the theme from 'singing cowboy' Roy Rogers' TV show *Happy Trails* – hence the nostalgic Western artwork.

NIRVANA

On the day that Kurt Cobain turned up with the opening riff to 'Smells Like Teen Spirit', he made the band play it solidly for 90 minutes. 'I was trying to write the ultimate pop song,' he confessed. 'I was basically trying to rip off The Pixies ... being soft and quiet and then a loud riff.'

Nevermind was released on September 24, 1991. It has since become one of the most talked about and most imitated records ever recorded. Cobain responded to the success and ubiquity of *Nevermind* by decrying its sound and denying its brilliance. 'There was that punk rock guilt,' says Dave Grohl. 'Kurt felt, in some way, guilty that he had done something that so many people had latched onto.'

Courtesy of thisdayinmusic.com

PINK FLOYD

Atom Heart Mother gave Pink Floyd their first number one album, and enjoyed an 18-week chart run. Pink Floyd and designer Storm Thorgerson (from Hipgnosis) decided that the album sleeve should be as 'unpsychedelic as possible ... un-Floyd-like and completely off the wall'. Storm was inspired by talking to UK conceptual artist John Blake, who suggested a cow as an 'anti-art' statement. So Storm drove into the countryside and photographed the first cow he saw, a Holstein-Friesian, allegedly named Lulubelle III, and owned by Arthur Chalke of Potters Bar, Hertfordshire.

In the US, Capitol Records, in a campaign to break Pink Floyd, pasted Lulubelle's image on billboards on Sunset Strip, and sent leading rock critics and DJs inflatable plastic udders!

Courtesy of thisdayinmusic.com

THE ALLMAN BROTHERS BAND

'We took it to where Cream and the Grateful Dead took it, then added John Coltrane and Herbie Hancock to the mix and stirred it a bit,' said Butch Trucks, the Allman Brothers Band drummer. 'We were up in places that no one else was thinking about. When I hear people describe *Eat A Peach* as Southern Rock I get fighting mad.'

Capricorn Records commissioned cover art based on collectable postcards, featuring a large peach in a small truck and the legend 'The Kind We Grow In Dixie'. Trucks loved it, but hated the title, and 'Eat A Peach' ended up gaining its name from a phrase Duane Allman once used to an interviewer: 'Whenever I go south, I eat a peach for peace'.

Courtesy of thisdayinmusic.com

Sex Pistols

For a group who only released one proper album, the Sex Pistols made one hell of an impact. *Never Mind The Bollocks...* was born amid the bloated pomp of progressive rock, a movement whose musicians could not have been further removed from the original Pistols line-up of Johnny Rotten (vocals), Steve Jones (guitar), Glen Matlock (bass) and Paul Cook (drums).

Their timing was perfect: those dirty little punks couldn't keep off the front pages of the newspapers. The good citizens of Britain were about to celebrate the Silver Jubilee of Queen Elizabeth II, just as the Pistols came along to ruin the whole thing with songs longing for 'Anarchy in the UK', skewering 'fascist regimes' and sneering about Her Majesty.

Courtesy of thisdayinmusic.com

NEVER MIND THE BOLLOCKS

HERE'S THE

Sex PiSTOLS

Rolling Stones

Released in December 1969, *Let It Bleed* is regarded as a Stones classic. It features the shimmering guitar lines and apocalyptic lyrics of 'Gimme Shelter' and the stunning 'You Can't Always Get What You Want', helped by the London Bach Choir. It's also the first Stones album to feature guitarist Mick Taylor.

The artwork was inspired by the working title of the album, *Automatic Changer*. The surreal sculpture was designed by Robert Brownjohn, showing *Let It Bleed* being played by the tone-arm of an antique phonograph. The items stacked on the plate are: a tape canister, a clock face, a pizza, a tyre and a cake topped by figurines of the band members. The cake parts were prepared by then-unknown English cookery writer Delia Smith, who went on to become a popular TV chef.

ROLLING STONES LET IT BLEED

STONES · LET IT BLEED

The British singer-songwriter Nick Drake died in his sleep on November 25, 1974 at the age of 26. He had suffered an overdose of Tryptasol, an anti-depressant drug. Drake signed to Island Records when he was 20, while still a student at the University of Cambridge. He released his debut album, *Five Leaves Left*, in 1969. By 1972, he had recorded two more albums – *Bryter Layter* and *Pink Moon*. Neither sold more than 5,000 copies on initial release. Nick Drake's reluctance to perform live, or even be interviewed, contributed to his lack of commercial success.

In 2000, Volkswagen featured the title track from *Pink Moon* in a television advertisement, and within a month Drake had sold more records than he had in the previous thirty years; he has posthumously become one of the most influential singer-songwriters of all time and a highly revered guitarist.

Courtesy of thisdayinmusic.com

Nick Drake

FIVE LEAVES LEFT

THE BEATLES

On September 26, 1969, The Beatles released *Abbey Road*, their eleventh album. At the time, the band all felt it probably would be the final Beatles product, and agreed to set aside their differences and 'go out on a high note'.

The cover photo was shot outside Abbey Road studios. Photographer Iain McMillan, balanced on a step-ladder in the middle of the street, took six photos of John, Ringo, Paul, and George walking across the zebra crossing while a policeman held up the traffic. The band then returned to the studio and recorded overdubs for the songs 'The End', 'I Want You (She's So Heavy)' and 'Oh! Darling'. The man standing on the pavement in the background is Paul Cole, an American tourist who was unaware that he was being photographed until he saw the album cover months later.

Courtesy of thisdayinmusic.com

The seventh album from the Electric Light Orchestra was the most successful yet for Jeff Lynne's musical ensemble, selling over ten million copies. Lynne wrote the entire album in just under a month, while living in a rented chalet in the Swiss Alps. The album was then recorded over two months in Munich.

'Mr Blue Sky' was released as a single, became a big hit and is now probably ELO's best-known song. It is the upbeat climax to a suite of music inspired by the torrential rainfall Lynne experienced while trying to write the album.

The spacecraft on the album's cover has been said to derive its inspiration from the docking spaceships in Stanley Kubrick's movie *2001: A Space Odyssey*: a suitably epic influence for Lynne's ambitious concept-album classic.

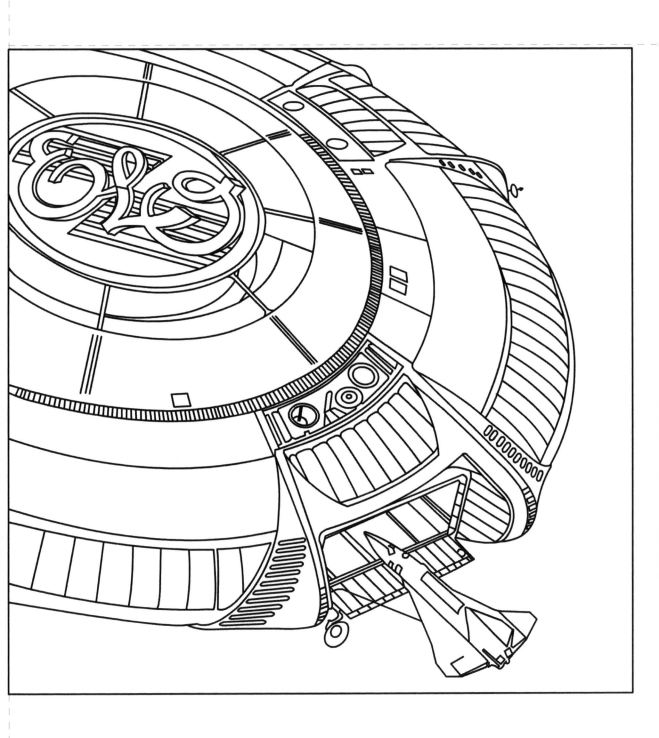

Supergrass

I Should Coco, the debut album from the power trio known as Supergrass, was a cheeky, chirpy kick in pop's backside back in 1995. It was perfect for the Britpop era: energetic punky songs with big harmonies, mischievous lyrics and irresistably feelgood, singalong hooks. Gaz Coombes (vocals and guitar), Danny Goffey (drums) and Mick Quinn (bass) clearly didn't take themselves too seriously, with zany videos portraying the three of them as madcap heirs to The Monkees. But they were musically adept beyond their young years: the album was an impressive blend of influences such as The Buzzcocks, The Jam, Madness, The Beatles and The Kinks.

The single 'Caught By The Fuzz' told a tale familiar to many: of being stopped by the police with a little bit of cannabis in your pocket. It was apparently based on something that Gaz Coombes experienced when he was 15. The album's title is Cockney rhyming slang, meaning 'I should say so'.

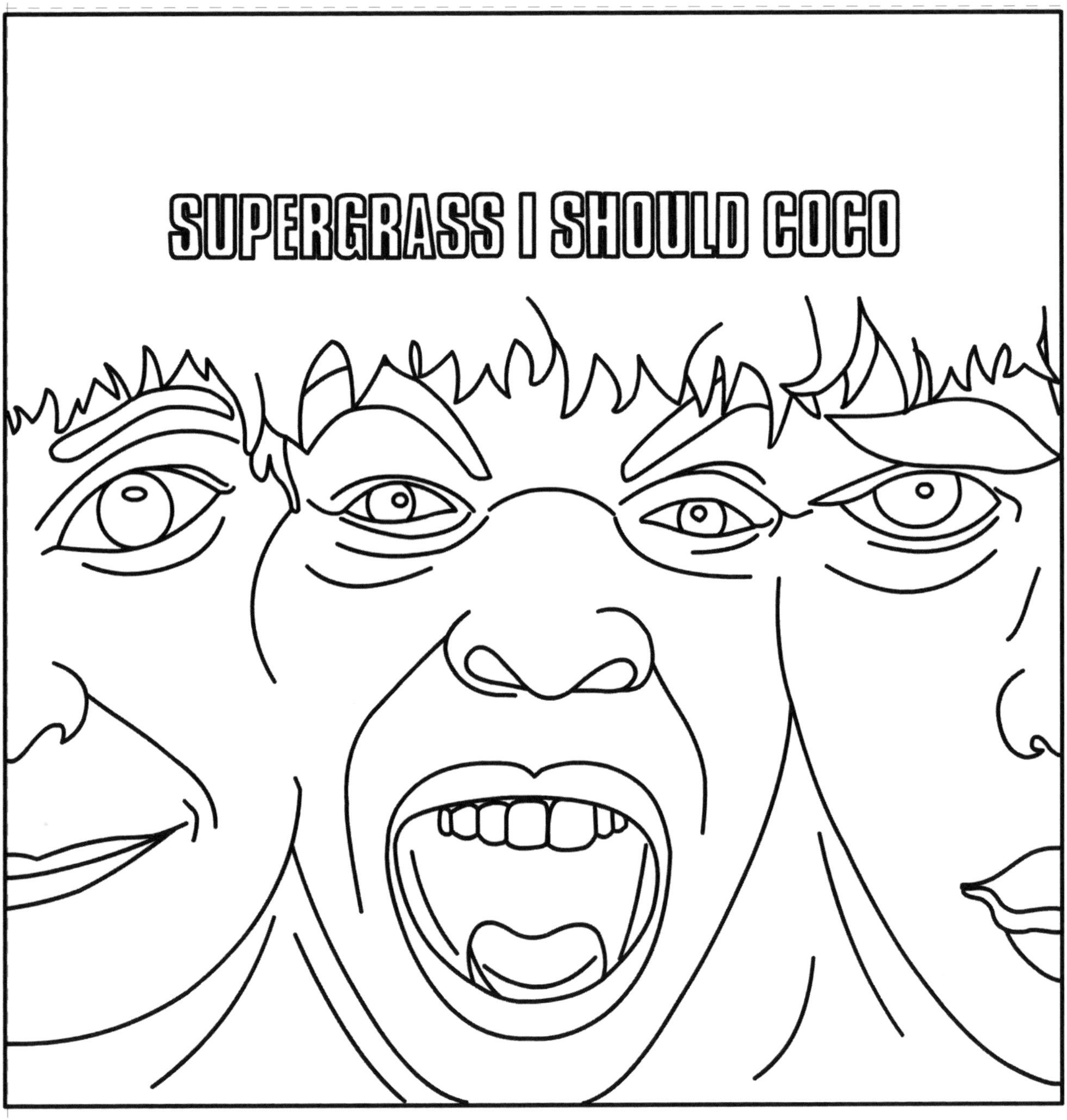
SUPERGRASS I SHOULD COCO

Stevie Wonder

Hotter Than July proved to be a big commercial success for Stevie Wonder when it was released in 1980. The album's first track, 'Master Blaster (Jammin')', was released as a single. It was inspired by reggae music and, more specifically, Bob Marley, who Wonder met and performed with at the Black Music Association in Philadelphia in 1979.

Another of the album's singles, the perky 'Happy Birthday', was dedicated to a different inspirational figure: Martin Luther King. The song had been written as a theme for the campaign to have King's birthday, January 15, decreed a national holiday in the US. Thanks to its extremely catchy chorus it has, for obvious reasons, become a staple of DJs and playlists at birthday parties across the world.

the 13th Floor Elevators

Credited with being the first use of the word 'psychedelic' in relation to music, *The Psychedelic Sounds...* was the debut album from The 13th Floor Elevators. The band were formed in Austin, Texas, in 1965 by guitarist and vocalist Roky Erickson, guitarist Stacy Sutherland and electric jug player Tommy Hall. Jug playing was a staple of old-time folk groups, but Hall's unusual vocalisations into his mic'd-up kitchenware ensured the Elevators sounded like no other rock band.

Their first single, 'You're Gonna Miss Me', has become a classic of garage rock, thanks to Roky Erickson's wailing vocals and savage harmonica playing: it's a key link between Sixties music and punk. The Elevators released four albums and Erikson has pursued a solo career, despite his suffering from both schizophrenia and maltreatment in several institutions.

'You gotta fight ... for your right ... to party!' screamed the Beastie Boys in 1986, over crunchy heavy metal guitars and a sledgehammer hip-hop beat. '(You Gotta) Fight For Your Right (To Party)' was the unforgettable, so-stupid-it's-genius fourth single to be taken from *Licensed to Ill*.

The Beastie Boys – MCA (Adam Yauch), Ad-Rock (Adam Horovitz) and Mike D (Michael Diamond) – started off as a punk band before switching to hip-hop. *Licensed to Ill*, their debut album, was a gloriously chaotic mess of pummeling drums, rock and funk samples and brattish, shouty raps. Many songs on *Licensed to Ill* have been accused of sexism, and the Beasties' tours at the time featured women dancing in cages and a motorised inflatable penis as a stage prop. Later albums from the boys' prolific career were both musically and lyrically more mature but, arguably, nowhere near as fun.

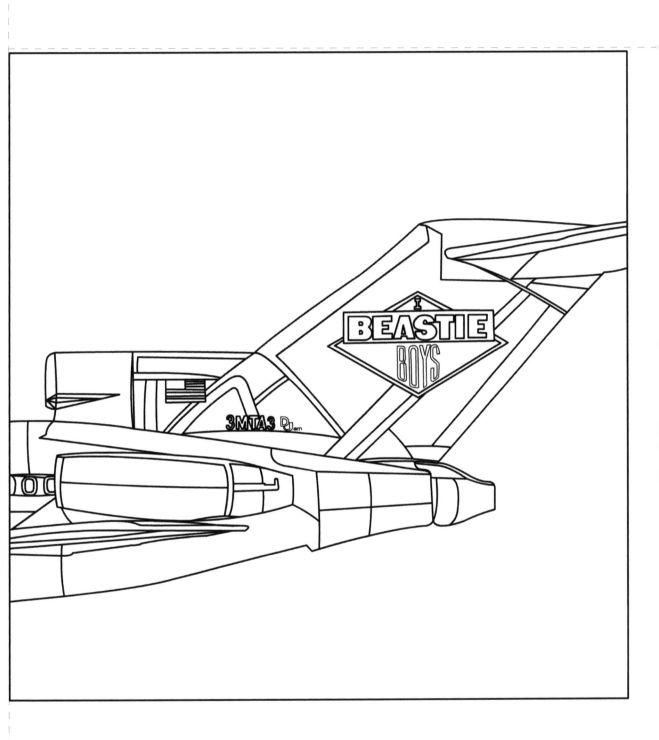

BRUCE SPRINGSTEEN

The seventh studio album from the New Jersey rocker became his most commercially successful, with fist-pumping good-time riffs and anthemic choruses. It established Bruce as one of America's favourite sons: a hard-working, blue-collar guy-next-door who wrote songs for people just like him.

But while the upbeat music, the US flag on the cover and the album's title seemed patriotic and celebratory, the album's lyrics told a different story. The politically charged title-track is critical of the Vietnam war, and concerns a troubled ex-serviceman struggling to find a job. '*Born in the U.S.A.* changed my life and gave me my largest audience,' Springsteen said. 'It forced me to question the way I presented my music and made me think harder about what I was doing.'

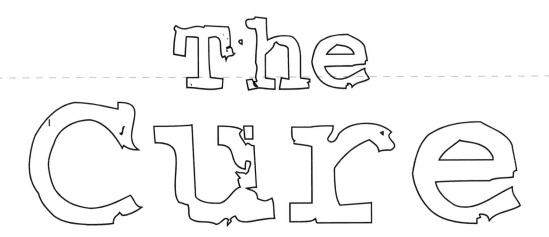

The Cure

Robert Smith, the heavily mascara-ed, wavy-haired lead singer, formed The Cure in Crawley, West Sussex, in 1976. Over the next few decades, across 13 albums, Smith has remained the only constant member, although Porl Thompson, Simon Gallup and Lol Tolhurst were part of the band for significant amounts of time.

They are often associated with Goth music – largely due to Robert Smith's morbid lyrics, theatrical image and the band's startling videos. But The Cure have flirted with many different musical styles: beginning as an arty post-punk band, they travelled in an inventive pop-orientated direction, with Smith's immediately recognisable yelping voice binding it all together. *Boys Don't Cry* was a studio album released in 1980; the title-track is one of rock's great unrequited love songs.

IT'S A BEAUTIFUL DAY

San Francisco in the late Sixties was a hotbed of hippy creativity. It was there that singer and violinist David LaFlamme, who had previously been a soloist for the Utah Symphony Orchestra, formed It's A Beautiful Day. He enlisted his wife Linda on keyboards and Pattie Santos on vocals, backed up by Hal Wagenet (guitar), Mitchell Holman (bass) and Val Fuentes (drums). Due in part to an unhappy relationship with their management company, It's A Beautiful Day never achieved the success of contemporaries such as Jefferson Airplane or the Grateful Dead – they were almost added to the bill for Woodstock, but lost out to Santana. However, their hit song 'White Bird' struck a chord with many and continues to be covered by other musicians, while regularly featuring in movie and TV soundtracks.

THE VELVET UNDERGROUND & NICO

Brian Eno once said that, while *The Velvet Underground & Nico* initially only sold 30,000 copies, "everyone who bought one of those 30,000 copies started a band". Mixing childlike Sixties pop with droning dissonance and feedback, it was ignored by the critics at the time, yet it became one of the most influential albums in rock. The Velvets line-up at the time was Lou Reed (vocals, guitar), John Cale (viola and bass), Sterling Morrison (guitar) and Maureen Tucker (drums). Nico (born Christa Päffgen) was a German singer and fashion model who had occasionally sang for the band, at the suggestion of Andy Warhol, the band's manager; her characteristic deadpan vocals lent an air of decadence to songs such as 'I'll Be Your Mirror' and 'All Tomorrow's Parties'; and backing vocals on 'Sunday Morning'.

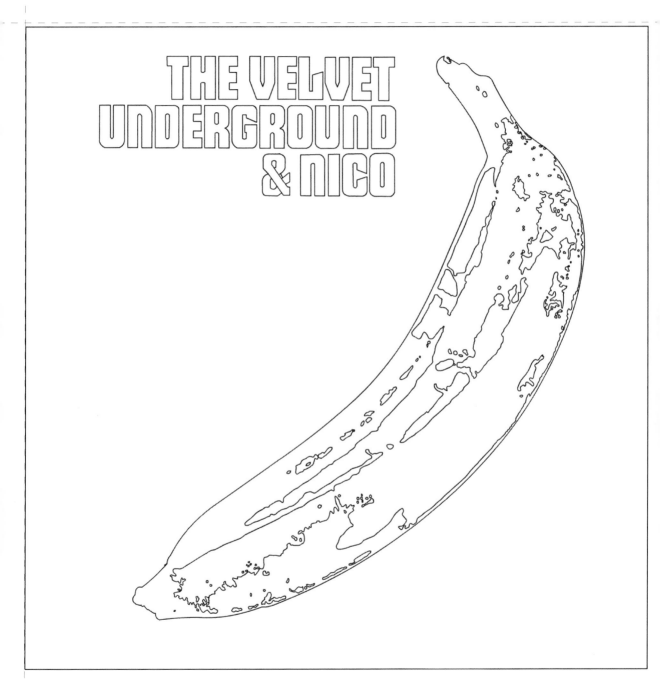

FRANK ZAPPA

AND THE MOTHERS OF INVENTION

Weasels Ripped My Flesh − surely one of the oddest album titles ever − is one of several albums documenting Frank Zappa's late-Sixties band The Mothers of Invention. It was released in 1970, a year after the group disbanded. On *Weasels...* the Mothers were a 12-piece − a rock band line-up with keyboards plus a full brass section, featuring Zappa on guitar on vocals. By turns terrifying and downright silly, the album's music lived up to the title and cover art, with complex jazz-funk orchestrations, fiery avant-garde jazz improvisation and alarmingly abrupt shifts in time signature, tempo and mood.

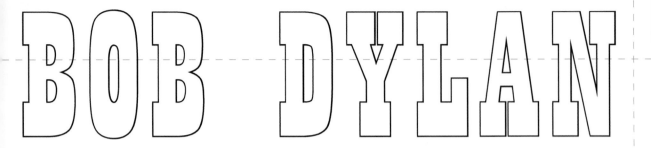

BOB DYLAN

Although he had occasionally used electric instruments on previous albums, *Highway 61 Revisited* heard Bob Dylan moving even further away from folk towards an R'n'B-flavoured sound. Bluesy electric guitar from Mike Bloomfield was heard to great effect on songs such as 'From a Buick 6' and the title-track, while 'Like a Rolling Stone' featured the rolling Hammond organ of Al Kooper. Honky-tonk piano and Dylan's harmonica gave the album the sound of a ramshackle bar-room band – albeit a very poetic and romantic one. It's a hugely influential album, which practically invented the 'Americana' genre: a wistful masterpiece of rootsy rock.

The photograph of Dylan was taken by Daniel Kramer in the entrance to the flat where Albert Grossman, Bob's manager, lived. Apparently Bob insisted on changing into his new Triumph Motorcycles T-shirt. Kramer felt the background was too "naked", and asked Bob Neuwirth, a friend of Dylan's, to stand there. Neuwirth was given a camera to hold, resulting in an extremely stylish, cryptic and sly album cover.

DEREK AND THE DOMINOES

After guitarist Eric Clapton had left the blues-rock supergroup Blind Faith, he put together Derek and the Dominoes with Bobby Whitlock (keyboards and vocals), Carl Radle (bass) and Jim Gordon (drums). All of them had previously played for Delaney & Bonnie, and also on George Harrison's double-album *All Things Must Pass*. 'I was in absolute awe of these people,' Clapton confessed of his fellow Dominoes. 'All we did was jam and jam and night would become day and day would become night, and it just felt good to me to stay that way. I had never felt so musically free before'.

Layla's title-track became Eric Clapton's most famous song, although it did not become a hit until 1972, two years after the album's release. An expression of unrequited love by Clapton about Patti Boyd, George Harrison's wife, 'Layla' possesses one of the all-time classic riffs, beloved of guitarists the world over.

DURAN DURAN

'Rio, to me, was shorthand for the truly foreign, the exotic, ' explained John Taylor, Duran Duran's bassist, who came up with the title. For him, it was 'a cornucopia of earthly delights, a party that would never stop'. *Rio* gave the group many of their best-loved hits, such as 'Save A Prayer', 'Hungry Like the Wolf' and 'The Chauffeur', helped by several memorable videos. The video for the title-track featured lead singer Simon Le Bon and the boys pouting to camera in radiant Caribbean sunshine on a luxury yacht, with the wind in their hair. It became one of the most enduring images of the glorious excesses of Eighties pop music. It wasn't all sun and fun however: during filming in Antigua and Sri Lanka, drummer Andy Taylor contracted a tropical virus that delayed Duran Duran's European tour.

This classic Eighties album featured cover art from Patrick Nagel, a painter who stamped his mark on Eighties design with his characteristic sharp lines and updated Art Deco influences.

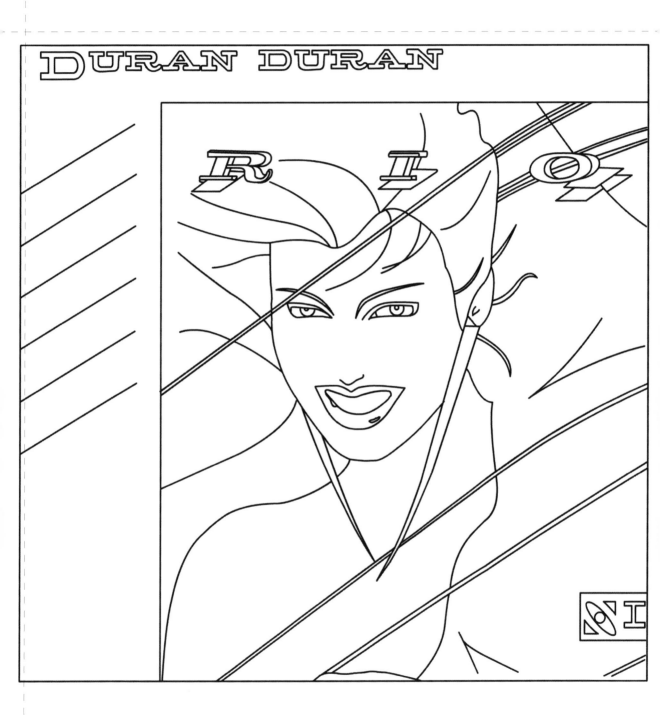

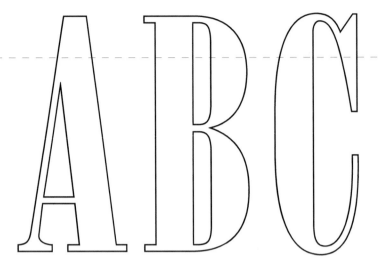

The Lexicon of Love was big in every sense. Released in 1982, it had highly orchestrated production, courtesy of Eighties über-producer Trevor Horn and Anne Dudley of the Art of Noise. It had melodramatic lyrics of desperate romance, belted out by the powerful vocals of singer Martin Fry. While its production was very much of its time, its songwriting harked back to the soul-pop of Motown and Sixties girl groups – albeit with a savvy Sheffield tongue in its cheek and a little post-punk irony lurking in its glossy pop choruses.

The album's hit singles just kept coming: 'Tears Are Not Enough', 'Poison Arrow', 'The Look of Love' and 'All of My Heart' remain staples of every Eighties disco night.

ELVIS COSTELLO

Three weeks after the release of *My Aim Is True*, in the summer of 1977, Elvis Costello (born Declan MacManus) was on the cover of a music paper. He described this situation as being 'an overnight success after seven years'. After all, he had been playing clubs and pubs in Liverpool and London since 1970.

It was not until he approached Stiff Records in 1976 that he received some interest, but even then it was only as a songwriter. He recorded some songs with the American group Clover as his band, initially as demos intended for Dave Edmunds. But they were too good for Stiff to pass over and so Costello recorded a whole album with Clover in a series of late-night sessions totalling around 24 hours. It was Stiff Records that gave him his stage-name and Barney Bubbles, Stiff's house designer, who made the striking, angular album cover.

DAVID BOWIE

Aladdin Sane was described by David Bowie as 'Ziggy goes to America' – a continuation of the Ziggy Stardust persona that he had adopted for his previous album – with the glam-rock guitar of Mick Ronson lighting up tracks such as 'Jean Genie'. Many of the lyrics were written during his 1972 US tour. 'Aladdin Sane was split down the middle,' he said, due to 'wanting to be up on the stage performing my songs, but on the other hand not really wanting to be on those buses with all those strange people.' However, he would later tell friends that the 'lad insane' in the album's title track was inspired by his brother Terry, who had been diagnosed as a schizophrenic.

It was Bowie who had the idea of the lightning bolt over his face on the cover, but the teardrop was apparently photographer Brian Duffy's doing. "He put that on afterwards, just popped it in there,' Bowie revealed. 'I thought it was rather sweet'.

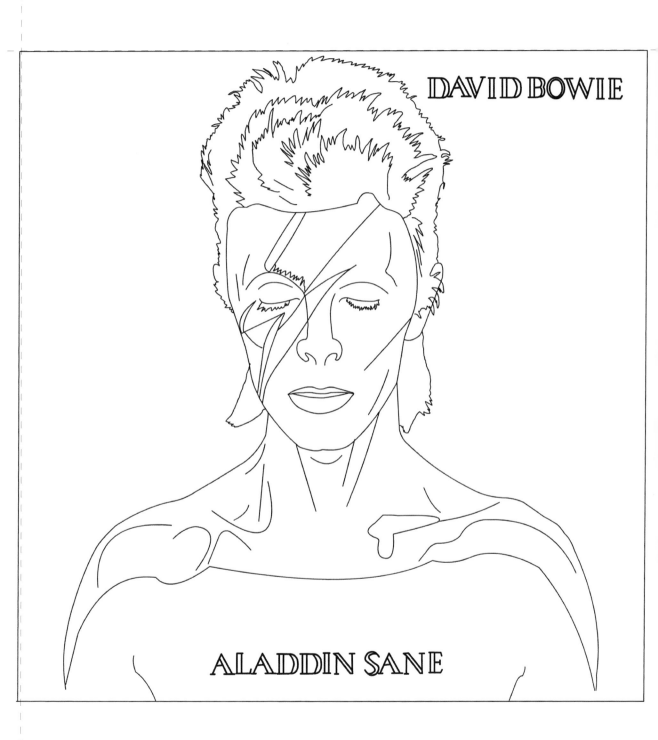

ERIC CLAPTON

The man revered as 'God' by his fans in the Sixties had been a heroin addict for three years. Eric Clapton admitted that he had done little other than watching television and getting out of shape. But, having kicked the habit, *461 Ocean Boulevard* proved to be a return to form, yielding a big hit in his cover of Bob Marley's 'I Shot the Sheriff'.

Robert Stigwood, Clapton's manager, paid for the rental house in the town of Golden Beach, near Miami where Clapton lived while recording the album; its address gave the album its name. It's a relaxed affair, paying tribute to many of Clapton's heroes of blues and R'n'B via cover versions of Robert Johnson's 'Steady Rollin' Man', Elmore James' 'I Can't Hold Out', Johnny Otis' 'Willie and the Hand Jive' and the traditional blues song 'Motherless Children'.

the EAGLES

'You can check out any time you like ... but you can never leave,' warned singer Don Henley on The Eagles' million-selling ode to the rock'n'roll lifestyle, 'Hotel California'. Despite its cautionary subject matter, the song's chiming guitars, high male harmonies and Spanish-tinged melody made it sound irresistibly sunny. A Seventies anthem, it's one of the all-time great driving songs.

Recorded between March and October 1976, the album's concept was described by Henley as: 'a little bicentennial statement, using California as a microcosm of the whole United States, or the whole world ... to try to wake people up and say 'We've been okay so far, for 200 years, but we're gonna have to change if we're gonna continue to be around'. It became the group's biggest-selling album to date; its cover photograph shows the Beverly Hills hotel.

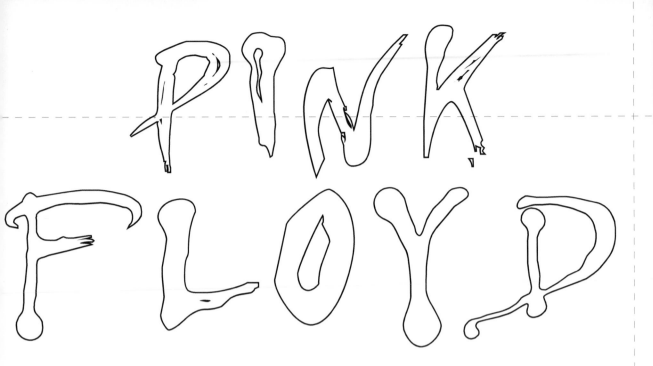

PINK FLOYD

1975's *Wish You Were Here* was Pink Floyd's ninth album. Its best-known track, 'Shine On You Crazy Diamond' was a heartfelt, moving tribute to their former lead singer, Syd Barrett, who had become a recluse due to mental illness. Other songs, such as 'Welcome to the Machine' and 'Have A Cigar' were scathing about the music industry's greed and cynicism, the latter song featuring the lyric 'by the way, which one's Pink?' – a question the group were often asked on tour.

Recorded at Abbey Road studios, the sessions were difficult and relations between the band members were strained. However, it has been cited by both Rick Wright and David Gilmour as their favourite Pink Floyd album, 'The end result of all that, whatever it was, definitely has left me an album I can live with very very happily,' Gilmour has said. 'I like it very much'.

Neil Young

'Good album,' Neil Young has said of 1974's _On The Beach_. 'One side of it particularly – the side with 'Ambulance Blues', 'Motion Pictures' and 'On the Beach', It's out there. It's a great take'. The overall sound of _On The Beach_ is quite unpolished. Allegedly, during the recording of the album, Young and some of his musicians consumed a homemade mixture they dubbed 'Honey Slides', a paste of marijuana marinaded in honey. Furthermore, Neil preferred the rough mixes his sound engineers provided, which did not endear him to them.

However, with songs as strong as 'Walk On', 'Vampire Blues' and the much-covered title track, and stellar musicians such as David Crosby, Graham Nash, Levon Helm and Ralph Molina playing on them, _On The Beach_ couldn't fail: it's a bluesy, country-rock classic.

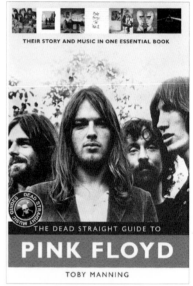
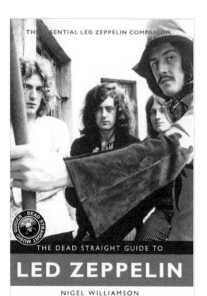

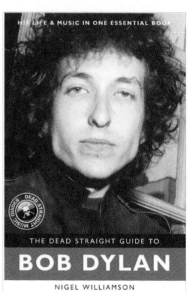

Printed in Great Britain
by Amazon